Mr Knight's gnome g

Mr Knight loved gnomes.
Even when he was
making bread, he was
dreaming of gnomes.

3

His friend Mr Knapp came to knock on his door. "I can help knead the bread," he said.

6

"Forget the bread," said Mr Knight. "I am going to design a garden full of gnomes. I will put a sign on my door so that people will know they can visit."

Mr Knight had one hundred
gnomes. There were
gnomes with red hats.

There was a gnarled
gnome, a gnome which
knelt on one knee and a
gnome that liked to knit.

"Great! I know where to put the gnomes in your garden. I hope you don't have rats. They would gnash and gnaw the gnomes," laughed Mr Knapp.

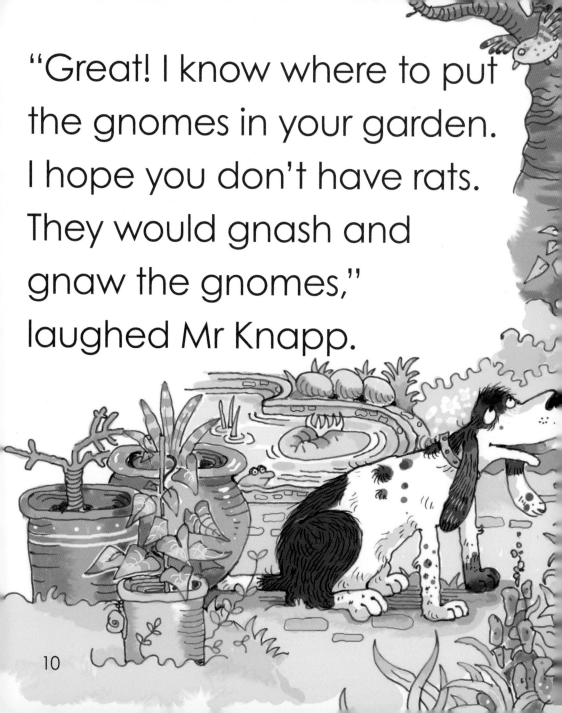

"Yes! Let's design my
gnome garden together,"
said Mr Knight.

Mr Knight and Mr Knapp put
gnomes beside the gnarled
tree. They put gnomes behind
the flowers and in the grass.

13

Mr Knight hung a sign
on his door knob.

Hundreds of people came.
"Wow!" they said.
"Great design!"

"I knew people would love our gnome garden!" said Mr Knight.

Words to blend

Knight	**Knapp**	**knead**
knock	**know**	**knelt**
knee	**knob**	**gnome**
design	**sign**	**gnarled**
gnash	**gnaw**	**knit**
knew	**behind**	**hundred**
flowers	**forget**	**grass**

Before reading

Synopsis: Mr Knight loves gnomes so much that he owns one hundred of them. He and his friend design a garden so that people can come and see them all.

Review phoneme and grapheme: /m/ mb

Focus phoneme: /n/   **Focus graphemes:** kn, gn

Story discussion: Look at the cover, and read the title together. Ask: *Have you ever heard of garden gnomes?* Talk about how some people put sculptures of gnomes in their gardens. Explain that Mr Knight in this story is mad about garden gnomes!

Link to prior learning: Briefly recap /m/ 'mb', and any Level 7 Set 2a graphemes that children need to practise. Remind children that the /n/ sound is often spelled 'n', but sometimes it's spelled 'kn' or 'gn'. Display the graphemes 'kn' and 'gn', and the words 'knee', 'sign', 'gnome' and 'know'. Ask children to read the words and sort them according to the spelling of the /n/ sound.

Vocabulary check: gnarled: knobbly, rough and twisted. Old trees often look gnarled.

Decoding practice: Turn to pages 8–9, and ask children to find and read the words where /n/ is spelled 'gn' and 'kn' (Knight, gnomes, gnarled, gnome, knelt, knee, knit).

Tricky word practice: Display the words 'Mr' and 'Mrs'. Tell children that these words are pronounced 'mister' and 'missiz'. Practise writing and spelling these words.

After reading

Apply learning: Can the children recall what happened in the story, and retell it briefly in sequence? Encourage them to use the pictures to help them, and to sum up the key events rather than reading every word on the page.

Comprehension

- Why does Mr Knapp visit Mr Knight in the first place? (He wants to help knead the bread.)
- What does he end up doing instead? (He helps Mr Knight design his gnome garden.)
- How many gnomes does Mr Knight have? (one hundred)

Fluency

- Pick a page that most of the group read quite easily. Ask them to reread it with pace and expression. Model how to do this if necessary.
- Turn to page 7. Ask children to read Mr Knight's words as expressively and fluently as possible, making it sound as if he's really speaking. Model a fluent reading for them, if necessary.
- Practise reading the words on page 17.

Tricky words review

Mr	Mrs	friend
to	said	people
watch	laughed	together
the	were	our
one	move	whole